Cricket™
Goes Camping

Written by

Robin Frederick and Jay Tverdak

Illustration by

Kathleen McCarthy

D1412006

Cricket's World

Cricket's world is full of fun and activity for Cricket and <u>you</u>. There are five other Activity Book and Tape sets like this one. And Cricket also has her own great Outfits—each one comes with a special cassette tape, too.

Cricket Activity Books and Tapes

1. Cricket's Clubhouse
2. Growing Up With Cricket
3. Cricket Takes a Vacation
4. Around the World with Cricket
5. Cricket Goes Camping
6. Holiday Fun with Cricket

Cricket Outfits and Tapes

1. School Time
2. Time for Outdoor Fun
3. Party Time
4. Indoor Play Time
5. Sleepy Time
6. Time for Health and Exercise

Hi, this is Cricket talking to you! Are we going to have fun or what?! There are so many things to do in this book, we better get started right away. You'll need crayons or felt pens, pencils, scissors, glue, tape and a few other things I'm sure you can find around the house.

Are you ready?
Alright! Let's go!

Here's a couple of snap shots of me—all ready to go camping. These two pictures look the same but they're not. Can you find five things about them that are different? (The answers are on page 24.)

D o you ever get the feeling you're being watched? Well, that's how I feel right now. Can you find the five hidden animals that are watching? (You can turn to page 24 for the answers—but I'd feel safer if you stayed right here.)

You can pretend you're hiking in your own backyard. The first thing you'll need is a backpack for all the important stuff you need to take along. So here's how you can make one.

You'll need:
    a double grocery bag (one inside another)
    some string
    scissors
    tape

Cut two penny-size holes near the top of the grocery bag. Make them about as wide apart as your shoulders are. Tape each hole inside and out to reinforce it. Cut two more penny-size holes near the bottom of the bag directly below the top two holes. Reinforce them with tape.

Run a string in to the bag through one of the top holes and out through the hole below it. Tie the ends of the string together. Do the same thing with the other two holes. Try on your backpack and shorten or lengthen the strings until the bag is snug against your back.

Now pack it with a sandwich and a map and you're ready for a hike!

Here's a hiking game you can play with a mirror. Lay this picture of Muddy Bog National Park on a table or dresser in front of a mirror. Looking in the mirror only, trace the hiking trail with your finger. It isn't easy!

There are five things in this picture that begin with the letter "T." Can you find them? (The answers are on page 24.)

9

It seems like every time I go hiking or camping I come back with my pockets full of interesting stuff—like shells and stones and twigs and pinecones. You know, you can start a nature collection with things like that.

All you need is:
    some empty egg cartons
    a pencil
    scissors
    tape
    small pieces of paper

Cut the lid off the egg carton. Place one object in each of the twelve egg holders. Tape a piece of paper to each holder. Label the object if you know what it is. Try to find out the names of the ones you don't know.

Keep your collection on permanent display in your room.

This camper brought a few things he certainly won't need. Can you find 7 things in this picture that don't belong in a campsite? (The answers can be found on page 24.)

After a long hike I love to sit in a peaceful spot like this and toss a few pebbles in the water. I even made up a game about it called "Pebbles in the Pond" that you can play.

You'll need:
  a piece of string
  15 pebbles

Tie the ends of the string together and lay it on the ground in the shape of a circle. Stand as far away from the circle as you are tall. (Lie down with your head touching the circle and mark where you feet are—that's where you should stand.) Now try to toss your pebbles into the circle. Score one point for every one that gets in (liners count) and two points for every pebble that lands in the circle, touching another one.

Here's a silly story game about some forest animals. Here's how you play it. Read the story. Each time you come to a blank, close your eyes and point to a word in the circle. Then read the word you've chosen.

Once upon a time in ____ city, there lived a beautiful ____ who married a handsome ____. Soon they had a cute little ____. Little ____, they called him 'cause he looked like a cross between a ____ and a ____ In fact, he had a face only a ____ could love. But he was the ____ of his Mother's eye!"

baboon
hippo
moose
deer
squirrel
warthog
turtle
frog
fish
snail

Here's a doll I learned how to make last time I went camping. My mom showed me and she said _her_ mom showed her. All you need is a handful of long grass, the longest you can find.

Gather the grass in a long straight bundle in your hand and fold it in half. Tie a strong blade of grass around the bundle just below the fold. This is the head and neck. Pull a few blades out from each side and trim them a little shorter than the rest. Wrap another blade around each end to make the arms. Trim the remaining grass so it makes a nice even skirt.

We went camping at the beach once. I especially loved that. When I got home I made a great shell collection and I had a lot of shells left over to make other neat things like this shell mobile.

You'll need:
   a piece of driftwood
   shells
   white glue
   yarn

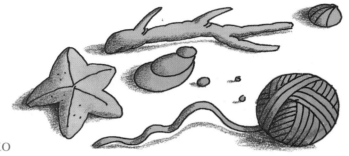

Cut the yarn into different lengths from six inches to twelve inches. Glue each shell to the end of a piece of yarn. Let the glue dry. Now tie the other end of the yarn to the piece of driftwood. Tie another piece of yarn to one end of the driftwood. Tie the other end of the yarn to the other end of the driftwood and use this to hang your mobile.

You can make a mobile with an interesting tree branch from the woods, too. Instead of shells, hang leaves and seeds and pieces of bark.

Here's a fun drawing game you can try.

You'll need:
    a book
    a pencil
    a piece of paper

Put the piece of paper on top of the book. Put the book on top of your head. Hold the book with one hand and with the other, try to draw a picture of a tree, like this:

Good Luck!

GOOD
LUCK!

Well, I'm all ready to go fishing and bring back a great cook-out dinner. Please help me find the path that will take me to my favorite fishing spot. Use your finger to trace the only path that will take me all the way there.

Here are the names of four animals. No, that's not the way they're really spelled. I scrambled the letters. See if you can unscramble them. The answers are on page 24 but you won't need 'em.

MOSOE

CORW

BARBIT

WOL

You can pretend you're camping out right in your own bedroom.

All you need is:
    an old sheet
    string
    some heavy books
    2 chairs

Place the chairs back to back a few feet apart. Tie one end of the string to the top of each chair. Hang the sheet over the string. Put some heavy books on each corner of the sheet to hold it in a tent-shape.

nswers:

Page 4.
1. one has corner torn off
2. one Cricket wears party shoes
3. one backpack has frying pan
4. one Cricket has a compass
5. one Cricket has a walking stick

Page 5.
1. a racoon
2. a squirrel
3. a deer
4. a fish
5. a rabbit

Page 9
1. tent
2. table
3. teapot
4. tree
5. tire

Page 12 & 13.
1. kitchen stove
2. four-poster bed
3. bird cage
4. lawn mower
5. harp
6. safe
7. fancy gown

Page 22.
1. Moose
2. Crow
3. Rabbit
4. Owl